# Contents

First published 2016 by Brown Watson
The Old Mill, 76 Fleckney Road,
Kibworth Beauchamp, Leic LE8 0HG

ISBN: 978-0-7097-2313-4

# My Little Book of Transport Stories

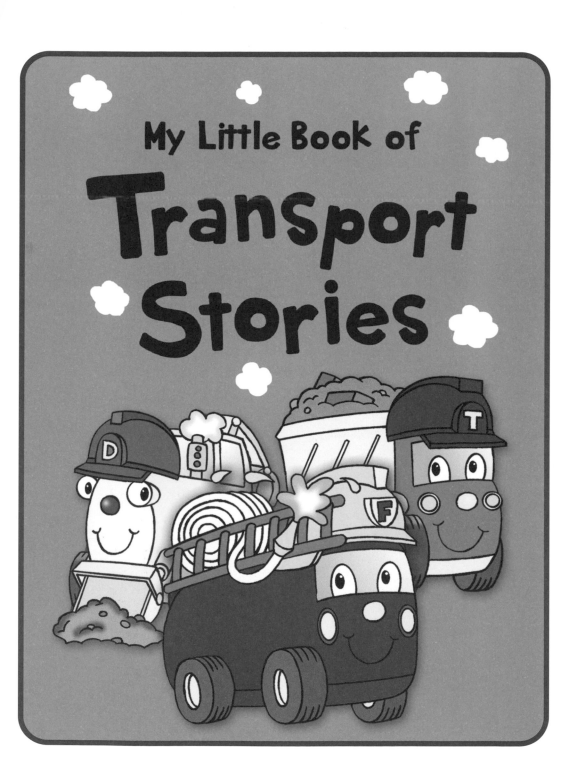

*Brown Watson*

ENGLAND

# Tom the Tractor

Tom the tractor is busy.
He works hard through the day.

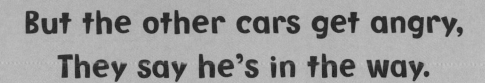

But the other cars get angry,
They say he's in the way.

"Why do you drive so slowly?
Why can't you let us past?"

8

"I'm sorry, guys," says Tom.
"But I am tough, not fast."

Tom keeps on chugging through grass and dirt and muck.

10

"You see? I must drive slowly,
Or else I'd just get stuck!"

# Finlay the Fire Truck

Finlay is a fire truck.
He's brave and has no fear.

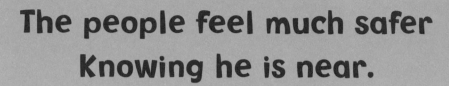

The people feel much safer
Knowing he is near.

"Finlay, help! My kitten
Is stuck up in a tree!"

It's an easy job for
Finlay to set the kitten free.

"Nee-naw!" goes his siren.
Finlay's on his way.

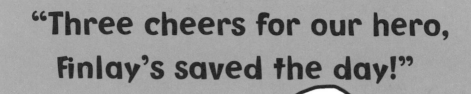

"Three cheers for our hero,
Finlay's saved the day!"

# Digby the Digger

"Come on chaps!" says Digby,
Working on the site.

"Our work today is tricky,
We need to get it right."

The friends all work together
Moving dirt around.

20

Soon they've dug a massive hole,
Deep into the ground.

"It's looking good!" says Digby.
The boss is happy, too.

"We've very nearly finished,
And that's all thanks to you!"

23

# Travis the Truck

Travis is a work truck,
He carries heavy loads.

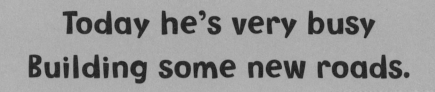

Today he's very busy
Building some new roads.

25

"Load me up!" shouts Travis.
"I'll carry all you need!"

He's soon filled up with rubble,
And trundles off at speed.

But Travis needs to slow down,
He's moving much too fast.

His load has tumbled
off his back,
The others can't get past!